Seerah Stories Out Loud!

Scan this QR code on your
smartphone or tablet for a free audio
reading of "The Young Man's Plan"

Need help?
Visit www.education-enriched.co.uk/audiobooks

~ For my children ~
R S KHAN

"The Young Man's Plan" is the first in a series of tales from the lives of the Companions. The series is aimed at inspiring Muslim children and instilling love in their hearts for those who were closest to the Messenger of Allah (may Allah's peace and blessings be upon him).

The reference for the events in this book are based upon the narrations found in the works: *ar-Raheeq al-Makhtum* by Sayf ur-Rahman Al-Mubarakpuri and *'Umar Ibn Al-Khattab: His Life and Times*, by Dr 'Ali Muhammad as-Sallaabee.

Disclaimer: The illustrations contained in this storybook are not intended to be accurate depictions of the Companions (may Allah be pleased with them). Additionally, efforts have been made to make it clear that the Prophet (may Allah's peace and blessings be upon him) has not been depicted in any form.

First published in 2014 by Education Enriched
Second edition published in 2016
www.education-enriched.co.uk

ISBN: 978-0-9930436-4-2

Printed in Croatia

The Young Man's Plan

Written by R S Khan

Illustrated by N Pilavci

PUBLISHED BY EDUCATION ENRICHED

This is the tale of a fearless young man,

Who thought of a wicked and horrible plan:

To harm a great prophet

Who was kind and sincere.

What a terrible plot!

What an evil idea!

He was known in the land to be fearsome and strong.

He did not like Islam, he believed it was wrong.

So he set out one day with a sword in his hand,

To carry out what he had wickedly planned:

To harm a great prophet

Who was kind and sincere.

What a terrible plot!

What an evil idea!

He was met by his friend, Nu'aym, on the way,

On that scorching hot, sizzling hot, stifling hot day.

"Where are you going?" Nu'aym asked the man,

And the man told his friend of his frightful plan:

To harm a great prophet

Who was kind and sincere.

What a terrible plot!

What an evil idea!

"What a bad idea that is," Nu'aym boldly said,

Trying to stop him from going ahead.

"Why don't you see to your own family first?"

The man replied, "Which of them?" fearing the worst.

"Your sister is Muslim,

Her husband is too!"

Was this just a rumour?

Or could it be true?

To his own sister's house,

Stormed the heated young man,

In a fiery rage he'd forgotten his plan:

To harm a great prophet

Who was kind and sincere.

What a terrible plot!

What an evil idea!

As he came near he could hear something new,

Was that the Qur'an? His uneasiness grew.

He asked them ferociously,

"What was that sound?"

He was sure he'd heard someone reciting out loud!

They refused to say that they'd been learning Qur'an,

And that they'd accepted the deen of Islam.

The man, in his fury, then started to fight,

What a terrible way to misuse his own might!

Then with courage and strength, on that scorching hot day,

The two brave believers decided to say:

"We believe in Allah,"

the All-Wise,

the Most High,

Who created the moon

And the stars

And the sky!

Regretting his actions, the man asked to see,

The Qur'an they'd been learning, to which they agreed.

So he read the great words of Allah, the Most High.

Would the man now believe? Or would he still deny?

"Please guide me to Muhammad!"

Said the man right away,

So his relatives trustingly told him the way...

To a house near the Ka'bah, then strode the young man.

Had he remembered his horrible plan?:

To harm a great prophet

Who was kind and sincere.

What a terrible plot!

What an evil idea!

He knocked on the door with the sword in his hand.

The Muslims were scared of this fearless young man.

"What's the matter with you? Let him in!" a voice said.

To the Prophet (upon him be peace) was he led....

The Prophet (upon him be peace) asked him why
He had come to the house.
Can you guess his reply?

His answer was simple: "I want to believe."
Was this part of his plot? Was he trying to deceive?

The truth was that Allah had opened his heart,

And the man truly wanted to make a new start!

"Allahu Akbar!" all the Muslims cried out,

It was a joyful occasion, without any doubt!

And so you may ask, what became of this man,

After he entered the fold of Islam.

Allah helped this man become one of the best,

With a promise of Jannah he was truly blessed.

He now used his strength to stand up for Islam,

And he held in his heart the entire Qur'an.

He became a great ruler, Islam made him strong.

He was known as the one who can tell right from wrong.

His name is well-known from the East to the West...

It is 'Umar ibn ul-Khattaab!

Had you already guessed?

May Allah be pleased with this fearless young man,

Who read some great words from the noble Qur'an,

Then gave up his wicked and horrible plan:

To harm a great prophet who was kind and sincere,

And accepted Islam, when the truth became clear.

"Indeed, I am Allah. There is no God except Me, so worship Me and establish prayer for My remembrance."

(Surah TaHa 20:14)

This is one of the beautiful verses which touched the heart of 'Umar ibn ul-Khattaab (may Allah be pleased with him).